Editor
Lorin E. Klistoff, M.A.

Managing Editor
Karen Goldfluss, M.S. Ed.

Editor-in-Chief
Sharon Coan, M.S. Ed.

Cover Artist
Barb Lorseyedi

Art Director
CJae Froshay

Art Manager
Kevin Barnes

Imaging
Rosa C. See

Product Manager
Phil Garcia

Publisher
Mary D. Smith, M.S. Ed.

Practice Makes Perfect

Pre-Algebra

GRADE 3

Author
Robert W. Smith

Teacher Created Resources, Inc.
6421 Industry Way
Westminster, CA 92683
www.teachercreated.com
ISBN-0-7439-8633-4
©2004 Teacher Created Resources, Inc.
Reprinted, 2006
Made in U.S.A.

Teacher Created Resources

Table of Contents

Introduction..3
Practice 1: Number Sentences/Missing Terms/Boxes and Symbols.........................4
Practice 2: Number Sentences/Missing Terms/Boxes and Symbols.........................5
Practice 3: Math Facts/Addition and Subtraction..............................6
Practice 4: Math Facts/Addition and Subtraction..............................7
Practice 5: Math Facts/Multiplication...............................8
Practice 6: Math Facts/Multiplication...............................9
Practice 7: Math Facts/Multiplication..............................10
Practice 8: Missing Factors.......................................11
Practice 9: Missing Factors.......................................12
Practice 10: Relating Multiplication and Division.....................13
Practice 11: Relating Multiplication and Division.....................14
Practice 12: Families of Facts/Addition and Subtraction................15
Practice 13: Families of Facts/Multiplication and Division.............16
Practice 14: Number Sentences/Missing Terms/Variables.................17
Practice 15: Number Sentences/Missing Terms/Variables.................18
Practice 16: Multiplying with Three Factors.........................19
Practice 17: Multiplying with Three Factors.........................20
Practice 18: Multiplying with Three Factors.........................21
Practice 19: Algebraic Symbols....................................22
Practice 20: Algebraic Symbols....................................23
Practice 21: Evaluating Simple Expressions...........................24
Practice 22: Evaluating Simple Expressions...........................25
Practice 23: Evaluating Simple Expressions...........................26
Practice 24: Applying Algebra.....................................27
Practice 25: Applying Algebra.....................................28
Practice 26: Working with Equations................................29
Practice 27: Working with Equations................................30
Practice 28: Sequences...31
Practice 29: Patterns and Sequences................................32
Practice 30: Using Parentheses in Expressions........................33
Practice 31: Using Parentheses in Expressions........................34
Practice 32: Simple Functions.....................................35
Practice 33: Simple Functions.....................................36
Practice 34: Simple Functions.....................................37
Practice 35: Solving Equations Using Addition........................38
Practice 36: Solving Equations Using Addition........................39
Test Practice Pages..40
Answer Sheets...46
Answer Key...47

Introduction

The old adage "practice makes perfect" can really hold true for your child and his or her education. The more practice and exposure your child has with concepts being taught in school, the more success he or she is likely to find. For many parents, knowing how to help your children can be frustrating because the resources may not be readily available. As a parent it is also difficult to know where to focus your efforts so that the extra practice your child receives at home supports what he or she is learning in school.

This book has been designed to help parents and teachers reinforce basic skills with their children. Practice Makes Perfect reviews basic math skills for children in grade 3. The math focus is on pre-algebra. While it would be impossible to include all concepts taught in grade 3 in this book, the following basic objectives are reinforced through practice exercises. These objectives support math standards established on a district, state, or national level. (Refer to the Table of Contents for the specific objectives of each practice page.)

- number sentences
- missing terms
- boxes and symbols
- math facts
- missing factors
- algebraic symbols
- fact families
- variables

- evaluating simple expressions
- applying algebra
- working with equations
- sequences
- patterns
- parentheses in expressions
- simple functions
- solving equations

There are 36 practice pages organized sequentially, so children can build their knowledge from more basic skills to higher-level math skills. (*Note:* Have children show all work where computation is necessary to solve a problem.) Following the practice pages are six test practices. These provide children with multiple choice-test items to help prepare them for standardized tests administered in schools. To correct the test pages and the practice pages in this book, use the answer key provided on pages 47 and 48.

How to Make the Most of This Book

Here are some useful ideas for optimizing the practice pages in this book:

- Set aside a specific place in your home to work on the practice pages. Keep it neat and tidy with materials on hand.
- Set up a certain time of day to work on the practice pages. This will establish consistency. An alternative is to look for times in your day or week that are less hectic and conducive to practicing skills.
- Keep all practice sessions with your child positive and constructive.
- Help with instructions if necessary. If your child is having difficulty understanding what to do or how to get started, work through the first problem with him or her.
- Review the work your child has done. This serves as reinforcement and provides further practice.
- Pay attention to the areas in which your child has the most difficulty. Provide extra guidance and exercises in those areas. Allowing children to use drawings and manipulatives, such as coins, tiles, game markers, or flash cards, can help them grasp difficult concepts more easily.
- Look for ways to make real-life applications to the skills being reinforced.

Practice 1

Directions: Write the missing number represented by the square on the line below the number sentence.

1. $5 + 8 = \square$

2. $7 + 9 = \square$

3. $10 + 4 = \square$

_____

_____

_____

4. $7 + 5 = \square$

5. $3 + \square = 9$

6. $\square + 8 = 11$

_____

_____

_____

7. $\square + 10 = 13$

8. $9 + \square = 13$

9. $10 + \square = 14$

_____

_____

_____

10. $\square + 6 = 12$

11. $\square + 7 = 12$

12. $4 + \square = 14$

_____

_____

_____

13. $5 + \square = 12$

14. $\square + 3 = 12$

15. $8 + \square = 15$

_____

_____

_____

16. $\square + 11 = 13$

17. $\square + 4 = 13$

18. $6 + \square = 10$

_____

_____

_____

19. $5 + \square = 14$

20. $\square + 8 = 14$

21. $\square + 6 = 15$

_____

_____

_____

22. $7 + \square = 14$

23. $6 + \square = 17$

24. $\square + 4 = 11$

_____

_____

_____

Practice 2

Directions: Write the missing number represented by the square on the line below the number sentence.

1. 6 + 7 = ☐

2. 12 + 9 = ☐

3. 11 + 7 = ☐

_____

_____

_____

4. 17 + 4 = ☐

5. 3 + ☐ = 14

6. ☐ + 10 = 19

_____

_____

_____

7. 11 + ☐ = 22

8. ☐ + 7 = 21

9. ☐ + 10 = 18

_____

_____

_____

10. 20 + ☐ = 31

11. ☐ + 8 = 19

12. 6 + ☐ = 13

_____

_____

_____

13. 5 + ☐ = 19

14. ☐ + 9 = 17

15. ☐ + 9 = 20

_____

_____

_____

16. 7 + ☐ = 17

17. 12 + ☐ = 22

18. ☐ + 13 = 18

_____

_____

_____

19. 12 + ☐ = 19

20. ☐ + 15 = 21

21. ☐ + 9 = 16

_____

_____

_____

22. 15 + ☐ = 21

23. 12 + ☐ = 23

24. ☐ + 8 = 21

_____

_____

_____

Practice 3

Directions: Write the missing math fact on the line.

1. 7 + 8 = _____

2. 8 + 11 = _____

3. 11 − 9 = _____

4. 8 + 13 = _____

5. 13 − 4 = _____

6. 12 + 9 = _____

7. 14 + 8 = _____

8. 19 − 11 = _____

9. 8 + _____ = 11

10. _____ + 7 = 12

11. _____ − 8 = 13

12. 19 − _____ = 15

13. 10 + _____ = 17

14. _____ − 7 = 13

15. _____ − 5 = 11

16. 15 − _____ = 11

17. 8 + _____ = 17

18. _____ − 7 = 4

19. 17 − _____ = 12

20. 11 + 8 = _____

21. 17 − 9 = _____

22. 16 − _____ = 9

23. 16 − _____ = 14

24. 21 − 8 = _____

25. _____ + 7 = 13

26. 8 + _____ = 18

27. 13 + _____ = 16

28. _____ − 4 = 9

29. 13 − _____ = 6

30. 4 + 17 = _____

31. _____ − 6 = 9

32. 12 + _____ = 21

33. 17 − _____ = 11

Practice 4 ᘓ ᘓ ᘓ ᘓ ᘓ ᘓ ᘓ ᘓ ᘓ ᘓ ᘓ ᘓ

Directions: Write the missing math fact on the line.

1. $9 + 7 =$ _____

2. $10 + 13 =$ _____

3. $17 - 8 =$ _____

4. $11 + 9 =$ _____

5. $19 - 7 =$ _____

6. $13 - 4 =$ _____

7. $6 +$ _____ $= 19$

8. _____ $+ 9 = 22$

9. $16 + 5 =$ _____

10. $20 - 7 =$ _____

11. _____ $- 7 = 20$

12. $13 + 5 =$ _____

13. $19 -$ _____ $= 14$

14. _____ $+ 15 = 22$

15. $23 - 9 =$ _____

16. $18 -$ _____ $= 7$

17. $6 +$ _____ $= 12$

18. _____ $- 9 = 6$

19. $18 -$ _____ $= 11$

20. $13 + 8 =$ _____

21. _____ $- 6 = 21$

22. $19 -$ _____ $= 12$

23. _____ $+ 8 = 14$

24. $13 +$ _____ $= 25$

25. $26 -$ _____ $= 12$

26. $24 - 13 =$ _____

27. $13 -$ _____ $= 6$

28. $4 + 17 =$ _____

29. $17 -$ _____ $= 8$

30. _____ $- 9 = 13$

31. _____ $- 6 = 9$

32. $12 +$ _____ $= 21$

33. $22 -$ _____ $= 13$

Practice 5

Directions: Write the missing math fact on the line.

1. 7 x 8 = _____

2. 4 x 10 = _____

3. 11 x 3 = _____

4. 8 x 3 = _____

5. 5 x 6 = _____

6. 12 x 4 = _____

7. 8 x 6 = _____

8. 6 x 10 = _____

9. 3 x 4 = _____

10. 5 x 9 = _____

11. 7 x 4 = _____

12. 9 x 3 = _____

13. 7 x 6 = _____

14. 9 x 4 = _____

15. 5 x 8 = _____

16. 7 x 12 = _____

17. 8 x 9 = _____

18. 9 x 6 = _____

19. 4 x 8 = _____

20. 9 x 9 = _____

21. 6 x 8 = _____

22. 9 x 12 = _____

23. _____ x 5 = 40

24. _____ x 7 = 63

25. _____ x 8 = 56

26. _____ x 3 = 33

27. _____ x 6 = 54

28. _____ x 7 = 49

29. _____ x 9 = 81

30. _____ x 5 = 45

31. _____ x 8 = 32

32. _____ x 7 = 63

33. _____ x 8 = 72

Practice 6

Directions: Write the missing math fact on the line.

1. 9 x 8 = _____

2. 4 x 7 = _____

3. 8 x 5 = _____

4. 9 x 6 = _____

5. 7 x 7 = _____

6. 10 x 6 = _____

7. 5 x 7 = _____

8. 6 x 11 = _____

9. _____ x 8 = 40

10. _____ x 9 = 63

11. _____ x 9 = 45

12. _____ x 7 = 35

13. 4 x _____ = 44

14. 9 x _____ = 45

15. _____ x 9 = 36

16. _____ x 8 = 96

17. _____ x 7 = 63

18. _____ x 6 = 54

19. 7 x _____ = 49

20. _____ x 6 = 66

21. _____ x 8 = 48

22. 7 x _____ = 56

23. 7 x 9 = _____

24. _____ x 6 = 72

25. 6 x _____ = 24

26. _____ x 5 = 30

27. _____ x 7 = 28

28. 4 x _____ = 36

29. 8 x 9 = _____

30. _____ x 11 = 132

31. _____ x 6 = 36

32. 4 x _____ = 48

33. 9 x _____ = 108

Practice 7 ⋐ ⋑ ⋐ ⋑ ⋐ ⋑ ⋐ ⋑ ⋐ ⋑ ⋐ ⋑ ⋐ ⋑ ⋐

Directions: Write the missing math fact on the line.

1. 4 x 12 = _____

2. 9 x 7 = _____

3. 7 x 4 = _____

4. 6 x 3 = _____

5. _____ x 8 = 40

6. _____ x 9 = 63

7. 8 x 8 = _____

8. 7 x 12 = _____

9. _____ x 7 = 84

10. _____ x 12 = 60

11. 7 x _____ = 77

12. 8 x _____ = 96

13. _____ x 6 = 54

14. _____ x 9 = 81

15. 8 x 7 = _____

16. 9 x 6 = _____

17. _____ x 8 = 64

18. _____ x 9 = 108

19. _____ x 10 = 120

20. 5 x _____ = 55

21. _____ x 9 = 99

22. 6 x _____ = 60

23. 4 x 12 = _____

24. _____ x 8 = 32

25. 7 x _____ = 28

26. _____ x 7 = 63

27. 3 x _____ = 36

28. _____ x 2 = 22

29. 7 x 9 = _____

30. _____ x 12 = 144

31. _____ x 9 = 108

32. 7 x _____ = 49

33. 5 x _____ = 25

 #8633 Practice Makes Perfect: Pre-Algebra

Practice 8

Directions: Write the missing factor represented by the square or triangle on the line below the number sentence.

1. 9 x △ = 81

2. 8 x △ = 64

3. 12 x □ = 144

_____

_____

_____

4. 7 x △ = 49

5. 3 x △ = 9

6. □ x 11 = 121

_____

_____

_____

7. □ x 6 = 36

8. 10 x □ = 100

9. 9 x □ = 108

_____

_____

_____

10. △ x 10 = 120

11. △ x 13 = 39

12. 10 x □ = 150

_____

_____

_____

13. 4 x △ = 16

14. □ x 14 = 28

15. □ x 15 = 30

_____

_____

_____

16. 10 x △ = 130

17. 20 x □ = 100

18. △ x 25 = 75

_____

_____

_____

19. 10 x △ = 110

20. □ x 2 = 50

21. □ x 13 = 130

_____

_____

_____

22. 20 x △ = 40

23. 25 x △ = 50

24. □ x 20 = 60

_____

_____

_____

Practice 9

Directions: Write the missing factor represented by the square or triangle on the line below the number sentence.

1. $9 \times \triangle = 81$

————

2. $11 \times \square = 121$

————

3. $5 \times \triangle = 25$

————

4. $8 \times \square = 64$

————

5. $7 \times \square = 49$

————

6. $\triangle \times 7 = 49$

————

7. $5 \times \triangle = 100$

————

8. $\square \times 8 = 200$

————

9. $\square \times 10 = 200$

————

10. $10 \times \triangle = 130$

————

11. $\triangle \times 12 = 120$

————

12. $2 \times \square = 26$

————

13. $15 \times \square = 30$

————

14. $\square \times 10 = 150$

————

15. $\square \times 13 = 39$

————

16. $15 \times \triangle = 60$

————

17. $20 \times \triangle = 120$

————

18. $\triangle \times 25 = 125$

————

19. $15 \times \triangle = 75$

————

20. $\square \times 11 = 121$

————

21. $\square \times 12 = 144$

————

22. $30 \times \triangle = 60$

————

23. $25 \times \triangle = 75$

————

24. $\square \times 20 = 60$

————

Practice 10

Directions: Use your understanding of multiplication and division to determine the missing number.

1. 81 ÷ 9 = _____

2. 9 x _____ = 81

3. 48 ÷ 8 = _____

4. _____ x 6 = 48

5. 5 x _____ = 45

6. _____ ÷ 9 = 5

7. 56 ÷ 8 = _____

8. _____ x 8 = 56

9. _____ x 10 = 100

10. 100 ÷ _____ = 10

11. 36 ÷ 12 = _____

12. 3 x _____ = 36

13. 7 x _____ = 35

14. _____ ÷ 7 = 5

15. _____ x 6 = 72

16. 72 ÷ _____ = 12

17. 11 x _____ = 121

18. 121 ÷ 11 = _____

19. 99 ÷ _____ = 11

20. _____ ÷ 9 = 11

21. _____ ÷ 6 = 3

22. 6 x _____ = 18

23. 12 x _____ = 60

24. 60 ÷ _____ = 5

25. 63 ÷ _____ = 9

26. _____ ÷ 9 = 7

27. _____ ÷ 8 = 3

28. 8 x _____ = 24

29. 12 x _____ = 96

30. 8 x _____ = 96

Practice 11

Directions: Use your understanding of multiplication and division to determine the missing number.

1. $45 \div 9 =$ _____

2. $9 \times$ _____ $= 45$

3. $96 \div 8 =$ _____

4. _____ $\times 12 = 96$

5. $7 \times$ _____ $= 84$

6. _____ $\times 12 = 84$

7. $50 \div 2 =$ _____

8. _____ $\times 2 = 50$

9. _____ $\times 15 = 45$

10. $45 \div$ _____ $= 15$

11. $99 \div 11 =$ _____

12. $9 \times$ _____ $= 99$

13. $5 \times$ _____ $= 100$

14. _____ $\div 20 = 5$

15. _____ $\times 4 = 100$

16. $100 \div$ _____ $= 25$

17. $13 \times$ _____ $= 39$

18. $39 \div 13 =$ _____

19. $75 \div$ _____ $= 3$

20. _____ $\div 25 = 3$

21. _____ $\div 7 = 11$

22. $7 \times$ _____ $= 77$

23. $15 \times$ _____ $= 75$

24. $75 \div$ _____ $= 5$

25. $80 \div$ _____ $= 20$

26. _____ $\times 20 = 80$

27. _____ $\div 9 = 12$

28. $12 \times$ _____ $= 108$

29. $25 \times$ _____ $= 125$

30. $5 \times$ _____ $= 125$

Practice 12 ∂ ☙ ∂ ☙ ∂ ☙ ∂ ☙ ∂ ☙ ∂ ☙ ∂ ☙ ∂ ☙

Directions: Write the missing math fact on the line.

1. $7 + 8 = $ _____

2. $8 + 7 = $ _____

3. $15 - 8 = $ _____

4. $15 - 7 = $ _____

5. $13 - 4 = $ _____

6. $9 + 4 = $ _____

7. $13 - 9 = $ _____

8. $4 + 9 = $ _____

9. $7 + $ _____ $= 11$

10. _____ $+ 4 = 11$

11. $11 - 7 = $ _____

12. $11 - $ _____ $= 4$

13. $9 + $ _____ $= 16$

14. _____ $- 7 = 9$

15. _____ $- 9 = 7$

16. $16 - 9 = $ _____

17. $8 + $ _____ $= 17$

18. _____ $- 9 = 8$

19. $17 - $ _____ $= 9$

20. $9 + 8 = $ _____

21. $13 - 8 = $ _____

22. $5 + $ _____ $= 13$

23. $13 - $ _____ $= 8$

24. $13 - 5 = $ _____

25. _____ $+ 7 = 13$

26. $6 + $ _____ $= 13$

27. $13 - 7 = $ _____

28. _____ $- 7 = 6$

29. $18 - $ _____ $= 7$

30. $11 + 7 = $ _____

31. _____ $- 11 = 7$

32. $7 + $ _____ $= 18$

Practice 13

Directions: Write the missing math fact on the line.

1. $7 \times 8 =$ _____   2. $8 \times 7 =$ _____

3. $56 \div 8 =$ _____   4. $56 \div 7 =$ _____

5. $55 \div 11 =$ _____   6. $11 \times$ _____ $= 55$

7. $55 \div 5 =$ _____   8. _____ $\times 5 = 55$

9. $7 \times$ _____ $= 63$ 10. _____ $\times 9 = 63$

11. $63 \div 7 =$ _____   12. $63 \div 9 =$ _____

13. _____ $\times 12 = 48$ 14. $48 \div$ _____ $= 4$

15. $48 \div 12 =$ _____   16. $4 \times$ _____ $= 48$

17. $8 \times$ _____ $= 72$ 18. _____ $\div 9 = 8$

19. _____ $\times 9 = 72$ 20. $72 \div$ _____ $= 9$

21. $7 \times$ _____ $= 84$ 22. $84 \div 12 =$ _____

23. _____ $\div 7 = 12$ 24. $12 \times$ _____ $= 84$

25. $9 \times 12 =$ _____   26. $108 \div$ _____ $= 9$

27. _____ $\div 9 = 12$ 28. $12 \times$ _____ $= 108$

29. $12 \times$ _____ $= 132$ 30. $11 \times$ _____ $= 132$

31. $132 \div$ _____ $= 11$ 32. $11 \times 12 =$ _____

Practice 14 ꙮ

Directions: Write the missing number represented by the letter on the line below the number sentence.

1. $7 + 5 = n$

_____

2. $12 + 9 = a$

_____

3. $11 + 7 = c$

_____

4. $16 + 5 = n$

_____

5. $7 + b = 13$

_____

6. $a + 11 = 19$

_____

7. $12 - b = 7$

_____

8. $17 + 7 = t$

_____

9. $x - 13 = 3$

_____

10. $7 + c = 13$

_____

11. $n - 9 = 7$

_____

12. $6 + 14 = a$

_____

13. $13 - 4 = m$

_____

14. $d - 5 = 12$

_____

15. $20 - c = 10$

_____

16. $n + 9 = 17$

_____

17. $9 + b = 21$

_____

18. $22 - 12 = s$

_____

19. $p - 11 = 7$

_____

20. $13 + t = 18$

_____

21. $n + 12 = 15$

_____

22. $18 - b = 12$

_____

23. $13 + b = 21$

_____

24. $n - 7 = 8$

_____

Practice 15

Directions: Write the missing number represented by the letter on the line below the number sentence.

1. $9 \times 8 = n$

_____

2. $3 \times 6 = c$

_____

3. $12 \times 7 = b$

_____

4. $8 \times 6 = x$

_____

5. $9 \times t = 27$

_____

6. $c \times 4 = 36$

_____

7. $2 \times b = 22$

_____

8. $8 \times 7 = d$

_____

9. $7 \times 9 = p$

_____

10. $6 \times c = 36$

_____

11. $t \times 9 = 45$

_____

12. $5 \times 10 = n$

_____

13. $8 \times 5 = d$

_____

14. $s \times 4 = 12$

_____

15. $11 \times b = 44$

_____

16. $t \times 9 = 18$

_____

17. $9 \times 6 = p$

_____

18. $10 \times 11 = a$

_____

19. $p \times 8 = 56$

_____

20. $6 \times n = 72$

_____

21. $a \times 12 = 84$

_____

22. $8 \times t = 88$

_____

23. $7 \times a = 35$

_____

24. $c \times 7 = 49$

_____

Practice 16

Directions: Write the missing factor represented by the square or triangle on the line below the number sentence. The first one is done for you.

1. (4 x 3) x 2 = ☐
4 x 3 = 12
12 x 2 = 24
___24___

2. (5 x 3) x 2 = ☐

_____

3. (5 x 2) x 4 = △

_____

4. (7 x 3) x 2 = △

_____

5. 5 x (2 x 5) = ☐

_____

6. (8 x 2) x 2 = △

_____

7. (4 x 2) x 5 = ☐

_____

8. 7 x (2 x 3) = ☐

_____

9. (6 x 2) x 4 = △

_____

10. (3 x 3) x 3 = ☐

_____

11. 6 x (1 x 4) = △

_____

12. (6 x 5) x 2 = △

_____

13. (7 x 2) x 4 = ☐

_____

14. 8 x (3 x 3) = △

_____

15. 9 x (2 x 4) = ☐

_____

16. (3 x 5) x 4 = ☐

_____

17. (5 x 5) x 4 = △

_____

18. 6 x (2 x 3) = △

_____

19. 7 x (3 x 4) = ☐

_____

20. (4 x 6) x 3 = △

_____

21. (6 x 3) x 2 = ☐

_____

22. 7 x (5 x 2) = ☐

_____

23. (5 x 4) x 4 = △

_____

24. (8 x 3) x 2 = ☐

_____

Practice 17 ꙮ

Directions: Write the missing factor represented by the square or triangle on the line below the number sentence. The first one is done for you.

1. (5 x 3) x 3 = ☐
    5 x 3 = 15
    15 x 3 = 45
      45

2. (4 x 3) x 3 = ☐
_____

3. (6 x 2) x 3 = ☐
_____

4. (8 x 2) x 3 = △
_____

5. 6 x (3 x 5) = ☐
_____

6. (7 x 2) x 3 = ☐
_____

7. (5 x 2) x 9 = △
_____

8. 9 x (3 x 3) = ☐
_____

9. (7 x 3) x 3 = ☐
_____

10. (2 x 2) x 2 = △
_____

11. 4 x (3 x 3) = △
_____

12. (4 x 5) x 5 = △
_____

13. (8 x 3) x 2 = △
_____

14. 6 x (2 x 2) = ☐
_____

15. 7 x (3 x 4) = ☐
_____

16. (3 x 3) x 11 = ☐
_____

17. (4 x 7) x 2 = ☐
_____

18. 6 x (3 x 4) = △
_____

19. 5 x (4 x 2) = △
_____

20. (4 x 5) x 3 = △
_____

21. (4 x 6) x 2 = ☐
_____

22. 11 x (5 x 2) = △
_____

23. (4 x 4) x 4 = △
_____

24. (5 x 5) x 5 = ☐
_____

Practice 18

Directions: Write the missing factor represented by the square or triangle on the line below the number sentence. The first one is done for you.

1. 8 x (3 x 3) = △
3 x 3 = 9
8 x 9 = 72
____72____

2. (6 x 5) x 3 = △

_____

3. 8 x (3 x 4) = ☐

_____

4. (6 x 2) x 9 = ☐

_____

5. (6 x 5) x 4 = △

_____

6. (10 x 4) x 2 = ☐

_____

7. (8 x 5) x 2 = △

_____

8. 11 x (4 x 3) = △

_____

9. (7 x 5) x 2 = ☐

_____

10. (3 x 2) x 2 = △

_____

11. 9 x (5 x 2) = △

_____

12. (4 x 4) x 3 = ☐

_____

13. (5 x 5) x 10 = ☐

_____

14. 12 x (5 x 2) = ☐

_____

15. 9 x (3 x 2) = △

_____

16. (4 x 3) x 10 = △

_____

17. (5 x 5) x 5 = ☐

_____

18. 6 x (4 x 5) = △

_____

19. 7 x (3 x 2) = ☐

_____

20. (8 x 5) x 3 = ☐

_____

21. (7 x 7) x 2 = △

_____

22. 11 x (11 x 1) = △

_____

23. (6 x 3) x 4 = △

_____

24. (4 x 3) x 9 = ☐

_____

Practice 19 ꙮ ꙮ ꙮ ꙮ ꙮ ꙮ ꙮ ꙮ ꙮ ꙮ ꙮ ꙮ

Reminder
The following symbols are often used in algebra:

$=$ is equal to $\neq$ is not equal to

$>$ is greater than $<$ is less than

$(\ )$ parenthesis $/$ divided by

$(\ )(\ )$ back-to-back parentheses: must multiply

Directions: Do the operational work in each expression and write the answer. The first two are done for you.

1. $3 + 7 > 4$

     10 is greater than 4

2. $3(9) + 7$

          34

3. $5 < 9 + 2$

4. $5 + 4 = 9$

5. $(6)(8)$

6. $(3 \times 4) + 4$

7. $19 > 3 \times 6$

8. $(5)(9)$

9. $24/4$

10. $4 \times 3 = 6 \times 2$

11. $9 + 8 > 10$

12. $15 - 6 < 17$

13. $(4 \times 8) = 32$

14. $20/4 = 5$

15. $7 \times 6 \neq 15$

16. $44/4 > 5$

17. $(5)(12) = 60$

18. $12/4 < 10$

19. $6 + 15 > 12$

20. $18 - 6 = 6 \times 2$

Practice 20 ꙮ ꙮ ꙮ ꙮ ꙮ ꙮ ꙮ ꙮ ꙮ ꙮ ꙮ ꙮ ꙮ ꙮ

```
┌─────────────────────────────────────────────────────┐
│                     Reminder                          │
│   The following symbols are often used in algebra:    │
│      =  is equal to          ≠  is not equal to       │
│      >  is greater than      <  is less than          │
│      ( ) parenthesis         ÷  divided by            │
│      ( )( ) back-to-back parentheses:  must multiply  │
└─────────────────────────────────────────────────────┘
```

Directions: Do the operational work in each expression and write the answer. The first two are done for you.

1. 9 + 2 > 2 + 4

      11 is greater than 6

2. (5)(9) + 3

           48

3. 7 + 13 < 5 x 5

4. 24/4 < 18/2

5. (9)(11)

6. (5)(5) − 7

7. (3) > 1 + 1

8. (3)(9) − 13

9. 36/4

10. 3 x 8 = 6 x 4

11. 9 + 16 > 11 + 13

12. 28 − 9 < 30

13. 7 x 6 < 90

14. 20/2 = 2 x 5

15. 36/4 ≠ 10

16. (9)(6) ≠ 42

17. (7)(8) = 4 x 14

18. 12/3 > 3

19. (6)(0) < 1

20. 17 − 1 = 4 x 4

Practice 21

Reminder

- When you *evaluate* an expression, you compute its numerical value.
- Multiply a number next to a parenthesis times the number in the parenthesis.

$$6(8) = 48$$

- Multiply the numbers inside back-to-back parentheses.

$$(9)(8) = 72$$

Directions: Evaluate these expressions. The first one is done for you.

1. $2(7) + 3$

$14 + 3 = 17$

$\underline{\ 17\ }$

2. $(6)(10) + 5$

_____

3. $2(8) + 3$

_____

4. $5(4) - 7$

_____

5. $8(4) - 5$

_____

6. $(4)(3) - 1$

_____

7. $8 + 3 - 4$

_____

8. $16 - 4 + 3$

_____

9. $11 + 5 - 3$

_____

10. $5 + 3 + 4$

_____

11. $(9)(3)$

_____

12. $4(12)$

_____

13. $4(4) \times (2)$

_____

14. $5 + 7 - 3$

_____

15. $12/4$

_____

16. $(6 \times 4) - 3$

_____

17. $10(7)$

_____

18. $5 \times 3 \times 2$

_____

Practice 22

Reminder

- When you *evaluate* an expression, you compute its numerical value.
- Do the operation inside the parentheses before the rest of the expression.
- Multiply a number next to a parenthesis times the number in the parenthesis.

    $6(8) = 48$

- Multiply the numbers inside back-to-back parentheses.

    $(9)(8) = 72$

Directions: Evaluate these expressions. The first two are done for you.

1. $(5 \times 2) + 3$

$10 + 3 = 13$

___13___

2. $(7 \times 2) + 5$

$14 + 5 = 19$

___19___

3. $6(9) + 3$

_____

4. $8(4) - 9$

_____

5. $13 + (5 - 3)$

_____

6. $6 + 7 + 8$

_____

7. $(7 + 3) - 5$

_____

8. $(15 - 6) + 7$

_____

9. $(7)(4) - 9$

_____

10. $(6)(8) - 3$

_____

11. $9 + (3 + 9)$

_____

12. $15 - 8 + 6$

_____

13. $(6 - 5) + (4)$

_____

14. $8 + (9 - 5)$

_____

15. $16/8$

_____

16. $(9 \times 3) - 3$

_____

17. $10/2$

_____

18. $(7 \times 3) \times 2$

_____

Practice 23 ◗ ◔ ◗ ◔ ◗ ◔ ◗ ◔ ◗ ◗ ◔ ◗ ◔

Reminder

- When you *evaluate* an expression, you compute its numerical value.
- Do the operation inside the parentheses before the rest of the expression.
- Multiply a number next to a parenthesis times the number in the parenthesis.

$$6(8) = 48$$

- Multiply the numbers inside back-to-back parentheses.

$$(9)(8) = 72$$

Directions: Evaluate these expressions. The first one is done for you.

1. $(9 \times 2) - 3$

$18 - 3 = 15$

$\underline{\quad 15 \quad}$

2. $5 + (4 \times 5)$

$5 + 20 = \underline{\qquad}$

$\underline{\qquad}$

3. $(2 \times 8) + 3$

$\underline{\qquad}$

4. $9(9) - 8$

$\underline{\qquad}$

5. $(12)(12) - 4$

$\underline{\qquad}$

6. $(7)(9) - 12$

$\underline{\qquad}$

7. $(9 \times 3) - 4$

$\underline{\qquad}$

8. $(11 - 7) + 9$

$\underline{\qquad}$

9. $(6 - 5) + (4)$

$\underline{\qquad}$

10. $8 + (9 - 5)$

$\underline{\qquad}$

11. $13 + (4 + 10)$

$\underline{\qquad}$

12. $(16 + 4) - 13$

$\underline{\qquad}$

13. $13 + (8 - 2)$

$\underline{\qquad}$

14. $8 + 11 - 7$

$\underline{\qquad}$

15. $(8 \times 2) - 6$

$\underline{\qquad}$

16. $7 + (5 \times 4)$

$\underline{\qquad}$

17. $(2 + 4) - 6$

$\underline{\qquad}$

18. $(9 \times 8) - 20$

$\underline{\qquad}$

 #8633 *Practice Makes Perfect: Pre-Algebra*

Practice 24 ᘐ ᘓ ᘐ ᘓ ᘐ ᘓ ᘐ ᘓ ᘐ ᘓ ᘐ ᘐ ᘓ ᘐ ᘓ

Directions: Write an equation for each word problem. Use the equation to solve each problem. The first one is done for you.

1. A box had 24 jacks that were either silver or black. There were 9 silver jacks. How many black jacks were in the box?

   Equation: $n = 24 - 9$ or $n + 9 = 24$

   $n = 15$

   Solution: There were 15 black jacks.

2. Joseph won 15 marbles that were either red or black. He counted 7 of them that were red. How many black marbles did he win?

   Equation:

   Solution:

3. Alicia dealt 32 cards from a deck of 52 cards. How many cards were not dealt?

   Equation:

   Solution:

4. There were 36 pieces of pizza at Jerry's birthday party. Mitzi ate 7 pieces. How many pieces of pizza were left?

   Equation:

   Solution:

5. A class of 20 students were allowed to choose either an ice cream bar or a cookie for dessert. Seven of the students chose cookies. How many students chose ice cream bars?

   Equation:

   Solution:

6. Amy and Jeffrey have 23 CDs. Amy owns 16 of the CDs. How many CDs does Jeffrey own?

   Equation:

   Solution:

7. Jason and Dylan scored a total of 40 points in a basketball game. Jason scored 23 points. How many points did Dylan score?

   Equation:

   Solution:

Practice 25 ∂ ℰ ∂ ℰ ∂ ℰ ∂ ℰ ∂ ∂ ℰ ∂ ℰ ∂ ℰ

Directions: Write an equation for each word problem. Use the equation to solve each problem. The first one is done for you.

---

1. A box of 9 marbles costs 81¢. What is the cost of each marble?

    Equation: $n \times 9 = 81$

    $n = 9$

    Solution: Each marble costs 9¢.

---

2. A pack of 12 baseball cards costs $1.32. What is the cost of each card?

    Equation:

    Solution:

---

3. Brian saw a box of 9 rubber balls on sale for 25¢ each. What was the total cost of all 9 balls?

    Equation:

    Solution:

---

4. A collection of 35 marbles had 10 silver marbles. How many marbles were not silver?

    Equation:

    Solution:

---

5. Jonathan collected 30 insects for his science project. Only 16 of the insects were beetles. How many of his insects were not beetles?

    Equation:

    Solution:

---

6. Megan was given a bag of 50 candies that had 16 lollipops. How many of her candies were not lollipops?

    Equation:

    Solution:

---

7. Vanessa bought 10 beads at a cost of 23¢ each. How much did she pay for all 23 beads?

    Equation:

    Solution:

---

8. Daisy spent 99¢ for a bag of 9 lollipops. What was the cost of each lollipop?

    Equation:

    Solution:

Practice 26 ৩ ৫ ৩ ৫ ৩ ৫ ৩ ৫ ৩ ৫ ৩ ৩ ৩ ৫ ৫

Directions: Write the missing number represented by the box on the line below each number sentence.

1. 6 x 2 = 8 + ☐

2. 9 x 4 = 12 x ☐

3. 3 x 4 = 6 x ☐

4. 4 x 4 = ☐ x 8

5. 9 + 11 = ☐ x 5

6. 6 x 8 = 12 x ☐

7. 8 + 22 = 6 x ☐

8. 20 − 10 = ☐ + 8

9. 24 − 11 = ☐ + 6

10. 7 x 8 = 50 + ☐

11. 8 x 9 = 12 x ☐

12. 10 x 6 = 12 x ☐

13. 19 − 11 = 6 + ☐

14. 25 − 9 = ☐ x 4

15. 39 − 11 = ☐ x 7

16. ☐ x 8 = 16 + 8

17. 36 − 21 = 3 x ☐

18. 12 + 10 = ☐ x 11

19. 24 + 12 = ☐ x 6

20. 14 + 14 = 7 x ☐

21. 17 + 7 = ☐ + 8

22. ☐ x 3 = 25 + 2

23. 44 − 11 = 3 x ☐

24. 32 − 12 = ☐ + 9

Practice 27

Directions: Write the missing number represented by the box on the line below each number sentence.

1. $5 \times 2 = 7 + \square$

2. $6 \times 9 = 14 + \square$

3. $9 \times 5 = 5 \times \square$

_____

_____

_____

4. $5 \times 4 = \square \times 10$

5. $7 + 13 = \square \times 4$

6. $4 \times 8 = 16 + \square$

_____

_____

_____

7. $2 + 22 = 6 \times \square$

8. $30 + 10 = \square \times 5$

9. $25 - 13 = \square \times 6$

_____

_____

_____

10. $6 \times 8 = 50 - \square$

11. $8 \times 8 = 4 + \square$

12. $10 \times 8 = 50 + \square$

_____

_____

_____

13. $29 - 11 = 6 \times \square$

14. $35 - 6 = \square + 5$

15. $50 - 2 = \square \times 8$

_____

_____

_____

16. $\square \times 4 = 20 - 8$

17. $46 + 8 = 9 \times \square$

18. $50 + 13 = \square \times 7$

_____

_____

_____

19. $24 + 24 = \square \times 12$

20. $7 + 14 = 3 \times \square$

21. $29 + 7 = \square \times 9$

_____

_____

_____

22. $\square \times 5 = 23 + 2$

23. $55 - 11 = 4 \times \square$

24. $42 - 14 = \square \times 4$

_____

_____

_____

Practice 28 ∂ ℰ ∂ ℰ ∂ ℰ ∂ ℰ ∂ ℰ ∂ ∂ ℰ ∂ ℰ

Directions: Determine the missing number in each sequence below.

1. (2, 4, 6, 8, 10, 12, _____ , _____ , _____ , _____ , _____)

2. (1, 3, 5, 7, 9, 11, _____ , _____ , _____ , _____ , _____)

3. (1, 5, 9, 13, 17, _____ , _____ , _____ , _____ , _____)

4. (4, 8, 12, 16, 20, _____ , _____ , _____ , _____ , _____)

5. (0, 5, 10, 15, 20, 25, _____ , _____ , _____ , _____ , _____)

6. (1, 6, 11, 16, 21, 26, _____ , _____ , _____ , _____ , _____)

7. (16, 14, 12, 10, 8, _____ , _____ , _____ , _____)

8. (90, 80, 70, 60, _____ , _____ , _____ , _____ , _____)

9. (100, 200, 300, 400, _____ , _____ , _____ , _____ , _____)

10. (26, 36, 46, _____ , 66, _____ , _____ , _____ , _____)

11. (11, 22, 33, _____ , 55, _____ , _____ , _____ , _____ , _____)

12. (1, 2, 4, 7, 11, 16, _____ , _____ , _____ , _____ , _____)

13. (2, 4, 8, 16, _____ , _____ , _____ , _____)

14. (25, 50, 75, 100, _____ , _____ , _____ , _____ , _____)

15. (3, 6, 10, 15, 21, 28, _____ , _____ , _____ , _____ , _____)

Practice 29 ෬ ෬ ෬ ෬ ෬ ෬ ෬ ෬ ෬ ෬ ෬ ෬ ෬ ෬

Directions: Determine the missing shape letter, or number in each pattern or sequence below.

1. (△ , ○ , □ , △ , ○ , □ , _____ , _____ , _____)

2. (⬡ , △ , △ , ⬡ , △ , △ , _____ , _____ , _____)

3. A, B, C, A, B, _____ , _____ , B, _____ , _____ , _____ , _____)

4. (AA, BB, BB, AA, BB, BB, _____ , _____ , _____ , _____ , _____)

5. (18, 28, 38, 48, _____ , _____ , _____ , _____ , _____)

6. (LL, MM, NN, OO, PP, QQ, _____ , _____ , _____ , _____ , _____)

7. (○ , □ , □ , □ , ○ , □ , _____ , _____)

8. (R, SS, TTT, R, SS, _____ , R, _____ , _____ , _____ , _____)

9. (G, PP, PP, G, PP, _____ , _____ , _____ , _____ , _____)

10. (25, 50, 75, 25, _____ , 75, _____ , _____ , _____)

11. (OO, PPP, PP, QQQ, QQ, RRR, _____ , _____ , _____ , _____ , _____ , _____)

12. (10, 20, 30, 10, 20, _____ , 10, _____ , _____ , _____ , _____)

13. (5, 10, 20, 5, _____ , 20, _____ , _____ , _____)

14. (○ , □ , ○ , ○ , □ , ○ , ○ , _____ , _____)

15. (▽ , △ , △ , ▽ , △ , △ , _____ , _____ , _____)

Practice 30 ෙ ෙ ෙ ෙ ෙ ෙ ෙ ෙ ෙ ෙ ෙ ෙ

Reminder
- When you evaluate an expression, you compute its numerical value.
- Do the operation inside the parentheses before the rest of the expression.

Directions: Evaluate these expressions. The first one is done for you.

1. $(5 \times 3) - (3 \times 2)$

$15 - 6 = 9$

$\underline{\quad 9 \quad}$

2. $(5 + 6) - (4 \times 2)$

$11 - 8 = \underline{\quad\quad}$

$\underline{\quad\quad\quad}$

3. $(2 \times 7) + (3 + 5)$

$\underline{\quad\quad\quad}$

4. $(3 \times 9) - (8 \times 3)$

$\underline{\quad\quad\quad}$

5. $(3 \times 6) - (6 + 5)$

$\underline{\quad\quad\quad}$

6. $(4 \times 7) - (9 \times 3)$

$\underline{\quad\quad\quad}$

7. $22 + (8 \times 6)$

$\underline{\quad\quad\quad}$

8. $(5 \times 12) - (3 + 4)$

$\underline{\quad\quad\quad}$

9. $(8 \times 7) + 19$

$\underline{\quad\quad\quad}$

10. $(7 - 2) + (5 \times 2)$

$\underline{\quad\quad\quad}$

11. $19 - (2 \times 6)$

$\underline{\quad\quad\quad}$

12. $(9 \times 6) - 13$

$\underline{\quad\quad\quad}$

13. $(9 \times 6) - 14$

$\underline{\quad\quad\quad}$

14. $(9 + 2) - (2 \times 2)$

$\underline{\quad\quad\quad}$

15. $17 + (12 \times 3)$

$\underline{\quad\quad\quad}$

16. $(4 \times 7) - (4 + 4)$

$\underline{\quad\quad\quad}$

17. $28 - (5 \times 4)$

$\underline{\quad\quad\quad}$

18. $(4 \times 6) - 13$

$\underline{\quad\quad\quad}$

19. $(7 \times 3) - 4$

$\underline{\quad\quad\quad}$

20. $(14 - 6) + 13$

$\underline{\quad\quad\quad}$

21. $(9 \times 6) - (8)$

$\underline{\quad\quad\quad}$

Practice 31

Reminder

- When you evaluate an expression, you compute its numerical value.
- Do the operation inside the parentheses before the rest of the expression.

Directions: Evaluate these expressions. The first one is done for you.

1. (9 x 2) – (2 x 7)

    18 – 14 = 4

      ___4___

2. (7 + 9) – (3 x 3)

    16 – 9 = _____

    _____

3. (3 x 5) + (6 + 3)

    _____

4. (4 x 7) – (6 x 2)

    _____

5. (4 x 11) + (7 + 13)

    _____

6. (5 x 5) – (4 x 4)

    _____

7. 33 – (8 x 4)

    _____

8. (6 x 9) + (7 + 8)

    _____

9. (9 x 7) – 23

    _____

10. (11 – 2) + (5 x 4)

    _____

11. 44 – (6 x 6)

    _____

12. (7 x 8) – 16

    _____

13. (9 x 9) – 81

    _____

14. (9 – 4) + (3 x 3)

    _____

15. 39 – (11 x 3)

    _____

16. (7 x 7) – (4 x 6)

    _____

17. 88 – (9 x 9)

    _____

18. (7 x 6) – (3 x 4)

    _____

19. (7 x 12) – 5

    _____

20. (14 – 6) + 16

    _____

21. (8 x 6) – (9 x 2)

    _____

Practice 32 ◎ ◎ ◎ ◎ ◎ ◎ ◎ ◎ ◎ ◎ ◎ ◎ ◎ ◎ ◎

Directions: Use the rules to find the missing numbers to complete each function frame.

1. *Rule:* Output = Input + 3

Input	Output
3	6
4	7
5	8
6	____
7	____
8	____

2. *Rule:* Output = Input + 6

Input	Output
3	9
5	11
6	12
7	____
9	____
12	____

3. *Rule:* Output = Input − 2

Input	Output
4	2
5	3
6	4
7	____
8	____
9	____
10	____

4. *Rule:* Output = Input + 7

Input	Output
4	11
6	13
8	15
10	____
12	____
14	____
17	____

5. *Rule:* Output = Input x 2

Input	Output
2	4
3	6
5	10
7	____
8	____
9	____
11	____

6. *Rule:* Output = Input − 7

Input	Output
7	0
8	1
9	2
12	____
14	____
15	____
16	____

7. *Rule:* Output = Input x 3

Input	Output
3	9
4	12
5	____
6	18
7	____
8	____
9	____

8. *Rule:* Output = Input + 4

Input	Output
2	6
4	8
6	____
8	____
10	14
12	____
14	____

#8633 Practice Makes Perfect: Pre-Algebra

Practice 33

Directions: Use the rules to find the missing numbers to complete each function frame.

1. *Rule:* Output = Input + 2

Input	Output
2	4
3	5
4	6
5	____
6	____
7	____
8	____

2. *Rule:* Output = Input − 2

Input	Output
2	0
3	1
4	2
5	____
6	____
7	____
8	____

3. *Rule:* Output = Input + 1

Input	Output
1	2
2	3
3	4
4	____
5	____
6	____
7	____

4. *Rule:* Output = Input − 5

Input	Output
5	0
6	1
7	2
8	____
9	____
10	____
11	____

5. *Rule:* Output = Input x 3

Input	Output
1	3
2	6
3	9
5	____
7	____
8	____
9	____
12	____

6. *Rule:* Output = Input − 4

Input	Output
4	0
7	3
9	5
10	____
12	____
14	____
15	____
18	____

7. *Rule:* Output = Input + 10

Input	Output
2	12
3	13
4	14
5	____
6	____
7	____

8. *Rule:* Output = Input − 10

Input	Output
11	1
12	2
13	3
15	____
17	____
18	____

Practice 34

Directions: Use the rules to find the missing numbers to complete each function frame.

1. *Rule:* Output = Input x 2

Input	Output
3	6
5	10
7	___
8	___
9	18
11	___
12	___

2. *Rule:* Output = Input x 5

Input	Output
2	10
3	15
4	20
5	___
6	___
7	___
8	___

3. *Rule:* Output = Input x 10

Input	Output
1	10
2	20
3	___
4	___
5	50
6	___
7	___

4. *Rule:* Output = Input – 10

Input	Output
15	5
16	6
17	7
18	___
19	___
20	___
21	___

5. *Rule:* Output = Input x 4

Input	Output
1	4
2	8
3	12
4	___
7	___
8	___
9	___

6. *Rule:* Output = Input + 8

Input	Output
3	11
4	12
6	14
7	___
10	___
11	___
14	___

7. *Rule:* Output = Input – 11

Input	Output
20	9
23	12
24	___
25	14
27	___
30	___
31	___

8. *Rule:* Output = Input + 12

Input	Output
10	22
12	24
14	___
15	27
17	___
20	___
23	___

Practice 35

Reminder
Any number added to one side of an equation must be added to the other side.

$$n - 7 = 18$$
$$\underline{+7 \quad +7}$$
$$n \quad = 25$$
$$25 - 7 = 18$$

Directions: Solve these equations by adding the same number to both sides of the equation. The first one is done for you.

1. $n - 6 = 12$
$\underline{+6 \quad +6}$
$n \quad = 18$
$\underline{n = 18}$

2. $n - 4 = 10$
$\underline{+4 \quad +4}$
$n \quad =$
_____

3. $n - 5 = 10$

_____

4. $c - 6 = 13$

_____

5. $b - 9 = 4$

_____

6. $n - 8 = 11$

_____

7. $a - 11 = 7$

_____

8. $d - 6 = 14$

_____

9. $n - 5 = 15$

_____

10. $t - 9 = 5$

_____

11. $s - 4 = 8$

_____

12. $d - 3 = 12$

_____

13. $r - 2 = 13$

_____

14. $c - 9 = 6$

_____

15. $n - 7 = 14$

_____

16. $s - 5 = 11$

_____

17. $n - 9 = 21$

_____

18. $d - 10 = 19$

_____

Practice 36

Reminder

Any number added to one side of an equation must be added to the other side.

$$n - 9 = 10$$
$$\underline{+9 \quad +9}$$
$$n \quad = 19$$
$$19 - 9 = 10$$

Directions: Solve these equations by adding the same number to both sides of the equation. The first one is done for you.

1. $n - 7 = 13$
$\underline{+7 \quad +7}$
$n \quad = \quad 20$
$\underline{n = 20}$

2. $n - 9 = 29$
$\underline{+9 \quad +9}$
$n \quad =$
_____

3. $t - 6 = 14$

_____

4. $d - 8 = 18$

_____

5. $n - 10 = 10$

_____

6. $c - 7 = 14$

_____

7. $t - 12 = 20$

_____

8. $b - 11 = 10$

_____

9. $s - 15 = 25$

_____

10. $n - 13 = 14$

_____

11. $x - 5 = 9$

_____

12. $r - 13 = 14$

_____

13. $n - 15 = 30$

_____

14. $d - 12 = 20$

_____

15. $t - 14 = 10$

_____

16. $n - 5 = 20$

_____

17. $p - 14 = 16$

_____

18. $b - 18 = 12$

_____

Test Practice 1 ᕲ ᕱ ᕲ ᕱ ᕲ ᕱ ᕲ ᕲ ᕱ ᕲ ᕱ

Directions: Determine the missing number for each blank below.

1. $12 + \underline{\hspace{1cm}} = 19$
- (A) 7
- (B) 6
- (C) 17
- (D) 31

2. $7 + \underline{\hspace{1cm}} = 15$
- (A) 18
- (B) 9
- (C) 8
- (D) 7

3. $\underline{\hspace{1cm}} - 10 = 5$
- (A) 5
- (B) 25
- (C) 15
- (D) 16

4. $\underline{\hspace{1cm}} + 13 = 17$
- (A) 6
- (B) 30
- (C) 4
- (D) 5

5. $\underline{\hspace{1cm}} - 8 = 17$
- (A) 25
- (B) 23
- (C) 9
- (D) 11

6. $9 + \underline{\hspace{1cm}} = 14$
- (A) 23
- (B) 5
- (C) 6
- (D) 4

7. $9 + \underline{\hspace{1cm}} = 21$
- (A) 12
- (B) 30
- (C) 13
- (D) 14

8. $\underline{\hspace{1cm}} + 14 = 23$
- (A) 9
- (B) 37
- (C) 11
- (D) 33

9. $\underline{\hspace{1cm}} + 6 = 15$
- (A) 10
- (B) 9
- (C) 18
- (D) 21

10. $\underline{\hspace{1cm}} + 13 = 29$
- (A) 17
- (B) 42
- (C) 32
- (D) 16

11. $4 \times 9 = \underline{\hspace{1cm}}$
- (A) 13
- (B) 36
- (C) 26
- (D) 48

12. $9 \times 8 = \underline{\hspace{1cm}}$
- (A) 17
- (B) 72
- (C) 27
- (D) 60

13. $8 \times 6 = \underline{\hspace{1cm}}$
- (A) 54
- (B) 46
- (C) 14
- (D) 48

14. $6 \times 9 = \underline{\hspace{1cm}}$
- (A) 15
- (B) 54
- (C) 64
- (D) 42

15. $8 \times 5 = \underline{\hspace{1cm}}$
- (A) 44
- (B) 48
- (C) 13
- (D) 40

16. $7 \times 7 = \underline{\hspace{1cm}}$
- (A) 14
- (B) 48
- (C) 49
- (D) 54

Test Practice 2

Directions: Determine the missing number for each blank below.

1. 7 x 8 = _____
- (A) 15
- (B) 54
- (C) 56
- (D) 48

2. 9 x 9 = _____
- (A) 18
- (B) 81
- (C) 48
- (D) 72

3. _____ x 10 = 50
- (A) 5
- (B) 10
- (C) 60
- (D) 6

4. 8 x _____ = 32
- (A) 8
- (B) 40
- (C) 4
- (D) 5

5. 7 x _____ = 63
- (A) 70
- (B) 9
- (C) 8
- (D) 54

6. 9 x _____ = 45
- (A) 54
- (B) 5
- (C) 6
- (D) 4

7. _____ x 7 = 21
- (A) 4
- (B) 7
- (C) 3
- (D) 28

8. _____ x 11 = 55
- (A) 5
- (B) 6
- (C) 11
- (D) 8

9. _____ x 7 = 56
- (A) 8
- (B) 9
- (C) 6
- (D) 63

10. _____ x 12 = 84
- (A) 7
- (B) 8
- (C) 9
- (D) 96

11. 72 ÷ 12 = _____
- (A) 84
- (B) 12
- (C) 9
- (D) 6

12. 96 ÷ 8 = _____
- (A) 14
- (B) 12
- (C) 9
- (D) 84

13. 12 x 12 = _____
- (A) 134
- (B) 24
- (C) 64
- (D) 144

14. 11 x 12 = _____
- (A) 121
- (B) 132
- (C) 64
- (D) 144

15. 8 x _____ = 88
- (A) 12
- (B) 18
- (C) 11
- (D) 10

16. _____ x 9 = 54
- (A) 6
- (B) 63
- (C) 7
- (D) 8

Number Sentences with Variables and Three Factors

Test Practice 3 ♪ ☺ ♪ ☺ ♪ ☺ ♪ ♪ ☺ ♪ ☺

Directions: Determine the value of the letter in each number sentence.

1. 9 x 3 = a
- (A) 17
- (B) 27
- (C) 24
- (D) 12

2. 4 x 3 = n
- (A) 14
- (B) 7
- (C) 16
- (D) 12

3. n x 11 = 66
- (A) 55
- (B) 5
- (C) 60
- (D) 6

4. 7 x d = 28
- (A) 8
- (B) 35
- (C) 4
- (D) 9

5. n x 4 = 44
- (A) 11
- (B) 48
- (C) 10
- (D) 54

6. 6 x n = 36
- (A) 30
- (B) 5
- (C) 6
- (D) 4

7. c x 7 = 49
- (A) 6
- (B) 7
- (C) 9
- (D) 14

8. 8 x p = 64
- (A) 8
- (B) 6
- (C) 9
- (D) 72

Directions: Choose the correct answer for each blank.

9. 2 x 3 x 4 = _____
- (A) 10
- (B) 24
- (C) 9
- (D) 42

10. 4 x 2 x 5 = _____
- (A) 14
- (B) 11
- (C) 42
- (D) 40

11. (3 x 4) x 3 = _____
- (A) 46
- (B) 15
- (C) 35
- (D) 36

12. 5 x (3 x 2) = _____
- (A) 32
- (B) 25
- (C) 10
- (D) 30

13. 5 x (4 x 3) = _____
- (A) 17
- (B) 23
- (C) 60
- (D) 35

14. (3 x 3) x 6 = _____
- (A) 12
- (B) 54
- (C) 64
- (D) 18

#8633 Practice Makes Perfect: Pre-Algebra © Teacher Created Resources, Inc.

Test Practice 4 ⟳ ⟳ ⟳ ⟳ ⟳ ⟳ ⟳ ⟳ ⟳ ⟳ ⟳ ⟳

Directions: Identify each algebraic symbol.

1. >
- (A) not equal
- (B) less than
- (C) greater than
- (D) equals

2. <
- (A) not equal
- (B) less than
- (C) greater than
- (D) equals

3. =
- (A) not equal
- (B) less than
- (C) greater than
- (D) equals

4. ≠
- (A) not equal
- (B) less than
- (C) greater than
- (D) equals

Directions: Evaluate these expressions.

5. 5 + 6 + 7
- (A) 18
- (B) 17
- (C) 77
- (D) 19

6. 8 (5) − 3
- (A) 10
- (B) 43
- (C) 37
- (D) 16

7. (16 − 4) + 7
- (A) 27
- (B) 19
- (C) 5
- (D) 20

8. (13 + 4) − 2
- (A) 15
- (B) 16
- (C) 19
- (D) 14

9. (9)(8)
- (A) 72
- (B) 17
- (C) 64
- (D) 56

10. (8 x 3) − 4
- (A) 21
- (B) 20
- (C) 7
- (D) 28

11. (19 − 6) + 3
- (A) 15
- (B) 16
- (C) 17
- (D) 10

12. (15 − 6) + 8
- (A) 18
- (B) 1
- (C) 17
- (D) 29

13. 7(9) − 7
- (A) 57
- (B) 56
- (C) 55
- (D) 9

14. (14 + 7) + 12
- (A) 32
- (B) 34
- (C) 33
- (D) 9

Test Practice 5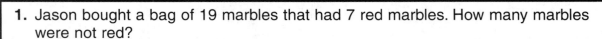

Directions: Choose the correct equation for each word problem.

---

1. Jason bought a bag of 19 marbles that had 7 red marbles. How many marbles were not red?

(A) $n - 19 = 7$

(B) $n - 7 = 19$

(C) $n = 19 - 7$

(D) $n \times 7 = 19$

---

2. Michael and Michelle have a total of 34 CDs. Michelle owns 19 of the CDs. How many CDs belong to Michael?

(A) $n - 34 = 19$

(B) $n \times 19 = 34$

(C) $n - 19 = 34$

(D) $n = 34 - 19$

Directions: Determine the missing number in each sequence or pattern.

---

3. (3, 6, 9, 12, _____)

(A) 16

(B) 15

(C) 14

(D) 21

4. (1, 6, 11, 16, _____ , 26)

(A) 21

(B) 20

(C) 36

(D) 18

---

5. (R, TT, R, TT, R, _____)

(A) S

(B) T

(C) TT

(D) RR

6. (A, B, C, A, B, C, _____)

(A) D

(B) A

(C) C

(D) B

Directions: Determine the value of the number that goes in each box.

---

7. $55 - 11 = 4 \times \boxed{}$

(A) 44

(B) 12

(C) 9

(D) 11

8. $3 \times 8 = \boxed{} \times 6$

(A) 8

(B) 5

(C) 4

(D) 24

---

9. $10 \times 6 = 5 \times \boxed{}$

(A) 10

(B) 12

(C) 9

(D) 60

10. $20 + 16 = \boxed{} \times 9$

(A) 4

(B) 38

(C) 5

(D) 36

Test Practice 6 ᵔ ᵔ ᵔ ᵔ ᵔ ᵔ ᵔ ᵔ ᵔ ᵔ ᵔ

Directions: Determine the value of the letter in each number sentence.

1. $n - 5 = 14$ Ⓐ 9 Ⓑ 19 Ⓒ 21 Ⓓ 12	**2.** $t - 13 = 21$ Ⓐ 34 Ⓑ 7 Ⓒ 8 Ⓓ 19
3. $s - 6 = 22$ Ⓐ 14 Ⓑ 16 Ⓒ 27 Ⓓ 28	**4.** $n - 20 = 13$ Ⓐ 7 Ⓑ 23 Ⓒ 6 Ⓓ 33
5. $n - 4 = 7$ Ⓐ 3 Ⓑ 12 Ⓒ 10 Ⓓ 11	**6.** $p - 11 = 30$ Ⓐ 29 Ⓑ 19 Ⓒ 21 Ⓓ 41

Directions: Find the missing number in each function frame.

7.

Input	Output		
3	4	Ⓐ	11
4	5	Ⓑ	9
6	7	Ⓒ	10
8	___	Ⓓ	7

8.

Input	Output		
3	6	Ⓐ	12
4	8	Ⓑ	13
5	10	Ⓒ	16
6	___	Ⓓ	14

9.

Input	Output		
5	11	Ⓐ	11
6	12	Ⓑ	16
7	13	Ⓒ	17
11	___	Ⓓ	15

10.

Input	Output		
12	8	Ⓐ	4
10	6	Ⓑ	3
9	5	Ⓒ	6
7	___	Ⓓ	11

11.

Input	Output		
1	3	Ⓐ	14
2	6	Ⓑ	16
4	12	Ⓒ	6
5	___	Ⓓ	15

12.

Input	Output		
41	31	Ⓐ	29
33	23	Ⓑ	18
26	16	Ⓒ	9
19	___	Ⓓ	10

Answer Sheet

Test Practice 1	Test Practice 2	Test Practice 3
1. Ⓐ Ⓑ Ⓑ Ⓓ	1. Ⓐ Ⓑ Ⓑ Ⓓ	1. Ⓐ Ⓑ Ⓑ Ⓓ
2. Ⓐ Ⓑ Ⓒ Ⓓ	2. Ⓐ Ⓑ Ⓒ Ⓓ	2. Ⓐ Ⓑ Ⓒ Ⓓ
3. Ⓐ Ⓑ Ⓒ Ⓓ	3. Ⓐ Ⓑ Ⓒ Ⓓ	3. Ⓐ Ⓑ Ⓒ Ⓓ
4. Ⓐ Ⓑ Ⓒ Ⓓ	4. Ⓐ Ⓑ Ⓒ Ⓓ	4. Ⓐ Ⓑ Ⓒ Ⓓ
5. Ⓐ Ⓑ Ⓒ Ⓓ	5. Ⓐ Ⓑ Ⓒ Ⓓ	5. Ⓐ Ⓑ Ⓒ Ⓓ
6. Ⓐ Ⓑ Ⓒ Ⓓ	6. Ⓐ Ⓑ Ⓒ Ⓓ	6. Ⓐ Ⓑ Ⓒ Ⓓ
7. Ⓐ Ⓑ Ⓒ Ⓓ	7. Ⓐ Ⓑ Ⓒ Ⓓ	7. Ⓐ Ⓑ Ⓒ Ⓓ
8. Ⓐ Ⓑ Ⓒ Ⓓ	8. Ⓐ Ⓑ Ⓒ Ⓓ	8. Ⓐ Ⓑ Ⓒ Ⓓ
9. Ⓐ Ⓑ Ⓒ Ⓓ	9. Ⓐ Ⓑ Ⓒ Ⓓ	9. Ⓐ Ⓑ Ⓒ Ⓓ
10. Ⓐ Ⓑ Ⓒ Ⓓ	10. Ⓐ Ⓑ Ⓒ Ⓓ	10. Ⓐ Ⓑ Ⓒ Ⓓ
11. Ⓐ Ⓑ Ⓒ Ⓓ	11. Ⓐ Ⓑ Ⓒ Ⓓ	11. Ⓐ Ⓑ Ⓒ Ⓓ
12. Ⓐ Ⓑ Ⓒ Ⓓ	12. Ⓐ Ⓑ Ⓒ Ⓓ	12. Ⓐ Ⓑ Ⓒ Ⓓ
13. Ⓐ Ⓑ Ⓒ Ⓓ	13. Ⓐ Ⓑ Ⓒ Ⓓ	13. Ⓐ Ⓑ Ⓒ Ⓓ
14. Ⓐ Ⓑ Ⓒ Ⓓ	14. Ⓐ Ⓑ Ⓒ Ⓓ	14. Ⓐ Ⓑ Ⓒ Ⓓ
15. Ⓐ Ⓑ Ⓒ Ⓓ	15. Ⓐ Ⓑ Ⓒ Ⓓ	
16. Ⓐ Ⓑ Ⓒ Ⓓ	16. Ⓐ Ⓑ Ⓒ Ⓓ	

Test Practice 4	Test Practice 5	Test Practice 6
1. Ⓐ Ⓑ Ⓑ Ⓓ	1. Ⓐ Ⓑ Ⓑ Ⓓ	1. Ⓐ Ⓑ Ⓑ Ⓓ
2. Ⓐ Ⓑ Ⓒ Ⓓ	2. Ⓐ Ⓑ Ⓒ Ⓓ	2. Ⓐ Ⓑ Ⓒ Ⓓ
3. Ⓐ Ⓑ Ⓒ Ⓓ	3. Ⓐ Ⓑ Ⓒ Ⓓ	3. Ⓐ Ⓑ Ⓒ Ⓓ
4. Ⓐ Ⓑ Ⓒ Ⓓ	4. Ⓐ Ⓑ Ⓒ Ⓓ	4. Ⓐ Ⓑ Ⓒ Ⓓ
5. Ⓐ Ⓑ Ⓒ Ⓓ	5. Ⓐ Ⓑ Ⓒ Ⓓ	5. Ⓐ Ⓑ Ⓒ Ⓓ
6. Ⓐ Ⓑ Ⓒ Ⓓ	6. Ⓐ Ⓑ Ⓒ Ⓓ	6. Ⓐ Ⓑ Ⓒ Ⓓ
7. Ⓐ Ⓑ Ⓒ Ⓓ	7. Ⓐ Ⓑ Ⓒ Ⓓ	7. Ⓐ Ⓑ Ⓒ Ⓓ
8. Ⓐ Ⓑ Ⓒ Ⓓ	8. Ⓐ Ⓑ Ⓒ Ⓓ	8. Ⓐ Ⓑ Ⓒ Ⓓ
9. Ⓐ Ⓑ Ⓒ Ⓓ	9. Ⓐ Ⓑ Ⓒ Ⓓ	9. Ⓐ Ⓑ Ⓒ Ⓓ
10. Ⓐ Ⓑ Ⓒ Ⓓ	10. Ⓐ Ⓑ Ⓒ Ⓓ	10. Ⓐ Ⓑ Ⓒ Ⓓ
11. Ⓐ Ⓑ Ⓒ Ⓓ		11. Ⓐ Ⓑ Ⓒ Ⓓ
12. Ⓐ Ⓑ Ⓒ Ⓓ		12. Ⓐ Ⓑ Ⓒ Ⓓ
13. Ⓐ Ⓑ Ⓒ Ⓓ		
14. Ⓐ Ⓑ Ⓒ Ⓓ		

Answer Key

Page 4
1. 13
2. 16
3. 14
4. 12
5. 6
6. 3
7. 3
8. 4
9. 4
10. 6
11. 5
12. 10
13. 7
14. 9
15. 7
16. 2
17. 9
18. 4
19. 9
20. 6
21. 9
22. 7
23. 11
24. 7

Page 5
1. 13
2. 21
3. 18
4. 21
5. 11
6. 9
7. 11
8. 14
9. 8
10. 11
11. 11
12. 7
13. 14
14. 8
15. 11
16. 10
17. 10
18. 5
19. 7
20. 6
21. 7
22. 6
23. 11
24. 13

Page 6
1. 15
2. 19
3. 2
4. 21
5. 9
6. 21
7. 22
8. 8
9. 3
10. 5
11. 21
12. 4
13. 7
14. 20
15. 16
16. 4
17. 9
18. 11
19. 5
20. 19
21. 8
22. 7
23. 2
24. 13
25. 6
26. 10
27. 3
28. 13
29. 7
30. 21
31. 15
32. 9
33. 6

Page 7
1. 16
2. 23
3. 9
4. 20
5. 12
6. 9
7. 13
8. 13
9. 21
10. 13
11. 27
12. 18
13. 5
14. 7
15. 14
16. 11
17. 6
18. 15
19. 7
20. 21
21. 27
22. 7
23. 6
24. 12
25. 14
26. 11
27. 7
28. 21
29. 9
30. 22
31. 15
32. 9
33. 9

Page 8
1. 56
2. 40
3. 33
4. 24
5. 30
6. 48
7. 48
8. 60
9. 12
10. 45
11. 28
12. 27
13. 42
14. 36
15. 40
16. 84
17. 72
18. 54
19. 32
20. 81
21. 48
22. 108
23. 8
24. 9
25. 7
26. 11
27. 9
28. 7
29. 9
30. 9
31. 4
32. 9
33. 9

Page 9
1. 72
2. 28
3. 40
4. 54
5. 49
6. 60
7. 35
8. 66
9. 5
10. 7
11. 5
12. 5
13. 11
14. 5
15. 4
16. 12
17. 9
18. 9
19. 7
20. 11
21. 6
22. 8
23. 63
24. 12
25. 4
26. 6
27. 4
28. 9
29. 72
30. 12
31. 6
32. 12
33. 12

Page 10
1. 48
2. 63
3. 28
4. 18
5. 5
6. 7
7. 64
8. 84
9. 12
10. 5
11. 11
12. 12
13. 9
14. 9
15. 56
16. 54
17. 8
18. 12
19. 12
20. 11
21. 11
22. 10
23. 48
24. 4
25. 4
26. 9
27. 12
28. 11
29. 63
30. 12
31. 12
32. 7
33. 5

Page 11
1. 9
2. 8
3. 12
4. 7
5. 3
6. 11
7. 6
8. 10
9. 12
10. 12
11. 3
12. 15
13. 4
14. 2
15. 2
16. 13
17. 5
18. 3
19. 11
20. 25
21. 10
22. 2
23. 2
24. 3

Page 12
1. 9
2. 11
3. 5
4. 8
5. 7
6. 7
7. 20
8. 25
9. 20
10. 13
11. 10
12. 13
13. 2
14. 15
15. 3
16. 4
17. 6
18. 5
19. 5
20. 11
21. 12
22. 2
23. 3
24. 3

Page 13
1. 9
2. 9
3. 6
4. 8
5. 9
6. 45
7. 7
8. 7
9. 10
10. 10
11. 3
12. 12
13. 5
14. 35
15. 12
16. 6
17. 11
18. 11
19. 9
20. 99
21. 18
22. 3
23. 5
24. 12
25. 7
26. 63
27. 24
28. 3
29. 8
30. 12

Page 14
1. 5
2. 5
3. 12
4. 8
5. 12
6. 7
7. 25
8. 25
9. 3
10. 3
11. 9
12. 11
13. 20
14. 100
15. 25
16. 4
17. 3
18. 3
19. 25
20. 75
21. 77
22. 11
23. 5
24. 15
25. 4
26. 4
27. 108
28. 9
29. 5
30. 25

Page 15
1. 15
2. 15
3. 7
4. 8
5. 9
6. 13
7. 4
8. 13
9. 4
10. 7
11. 4
12. 7
13. 7
14. 16
15. 16
16. 7
17. 9
18. 17
19. 8
20. 17
21. 5
22. 8
23. 5
24. 8
25. 6
26. 7
27. 6
28. 13
29. 11
30. 18
31. 18
32. 11

Page 16
1. 56
2. 56
3. 7
4. 8
5. 5
6. 5
7. 11
8. 11
9. 9
10. 7
11. 9
12. 7
13. 4
14. 12
15. 4
16. 12
17. 9
18. 72
19. 8
20. 8
21. 12
22. 7
23. 84
24. 7
25. 108
26. 12
27. 108
28. 9
29. 11
30. 12
31. 12
32. 132

Page 17
1. 12
2. 21
3. 18
4. 21
5. 6
6. 8
7. 5
8. 24
9. 16
10. 6
11. 16
12. 20
13. 9
14. 17
15. 10
16. 8
17. 12
18. 10
19. 18
20. 5
21. 3
22. 6
23. 8
24. 15

Page 18
1. 72
2. 18
3. 84
4. 48
5. 3
6. 9
7. 11
8. 56
9. 63
10. 6
11. 5
12. 50
13. 40
14. 3
15. 4
16. 2
17. 54
18. 110
19. 7
20. 12
21. 7
22. 11
23. 5
24. 7

Page 19
1. 24
2. 30
3. 40
4. 42
5. 50
6. 32
7. 40
8. 42
9. 48
10. 27
11. 24
12. 60
13. 56
14. 72
15. 72
16. 60
17. 100
18. 36
19. 84
20. 72
21. 36
22. 70
23. 80
24. 48

Page 20
1. 45
2. 36
3. 36
4. 48
5. 90
6. 42
7. 90
8. 81
9. 63
10. 8
11. 36
12. 100
13. 48
14. 24
15. 84
16. 99
17. 56
18. 72
19. 40
20. 60
21. 48
22. 110
23. 64
24. 125

Page 21
1. 72
2. 90
3. 96
4. 108
5. 120
6. 80
7. 80
8. 132
9. 70
10. 12
11. 90
12. 48
13. 250
14. 120
15. 54
16. 120
17. 125
18. 120
19. 42
20. 120
21. 98
22. 121
23. 72
24. 108

Page 22
1. 10 is greater than 4
2. 34
3. 5 is less than 11
4. 9 is equal to 9
5. 48
6. 16
7. 19 is greater than 18
8. 45
9. 6
10. 12 is equal to 12
11. 17 is greater than 10
12. 9 is less than 17
13. 32 is equal to 32
14. 5 is equal to 5
15. 42 is not equal to 15
16. 11 is greater than 5
17. 60 is equal to 60
18. 3 is less than 10
19. 21 is greater than 12
20. 12 is equal to 12

Page 23
1. 11 is greater than 6
2. 48
3. 20 is less than 25
4. 6 is less than 9
5. 99
6. 18
7. 3 is greater than 2
8. 14
9. 9
10. 24 is equal to 24
11. 25 is greater than 24
12. 19 is less than 30
13. 42 is less than 90
14. 10 is equal to 10
15. 9 is not equal to 10
16. 54 is not equal to 42
17. 56 is equal to 56
18. 4 is greater than 3
19. 0 is less than 1
20. 16 is equal to 16

Answer Key (cont.)

Page 24
1. 17
2. 65
3. 19
4. 13
5. 27
6. 11
7. 7
8. 15
9. 13
10. 12
11. 27
12. 48
13. 32
14. 9
15. 3
16. 21
17. 70
18. 30

Page 25
1. 13
2. 19
3. 57
4. 23
5. 15
6. 21
7. 5
8. 16
9. 19
10. 45
11. 21
12. 13
13. 5
14. 12
15. 2
16. 24
17. 5
18. 42

Page 26
1. 15
2. 25
3. 19
4. 73
5. 140
6. 51
7. 23
8. 13
9. 5
10. 12
11. 27
12. 7
13. 19
14. 12
15. 10
16. 27
17. 0
18. 52

Page 27
1. $n = 24 - 9$ or
   $n + 9 = 24$
   $n = 15$
   15 black jacks

2. $n = 15 - 7$
   or $n + 7 = 15$
   $n = 8$
   8 black marbles
3. $n = 52 - 32$ or
   $n + 32 = 52$
   $n = 20$
   20 cards not dealt
4. $n = 36 - 7$ or
   $n + 7 = 36$
   $n = 29$
   29 pieces of pizza were left.
5. $n = 20 - 7$ or
   $n + 7 = 20$
   $n = 13$
   13 ice cream bars
6. $n = 23 - 16$ or
   $n + 16 = 23$
   $n = 7$
   7 CDs owned by Jeffrey
7. $n + 23 = 40$ or
   $n = 40 - 23$
   $n = 17$
   17 points scored by Dylan

Page 28
1. $n \times 9 = 81$
   Each marble costs 9¢.
2. $n \times 12 = \$1.32$
   or $\$1.32/12 = n$
   Each card costs 11¢.
3. $n = 9 \times 25$
   $n = \$2.25$
4. $n = 35 - 10$ or
   $n + 10 = 35$
   25 marbles were not silver.
5. $n = 30 - 16$ or
   $n + 16 = 30$
   14 insects were not beetles.
6. $n = 50 - 16$ or
   $n + 16 = 50$
   34 candies were not lollipops.
7. $n = 10 \times 23$
   $n + \$2.30$
8. $n = 99/9$ or
   $n \times 9 = 99$¢
   $n = 11$¢

Page 29
1. 4
2. 3
3. 2
4. 2
5. 4

6. 4
7. 5
8. 2
9. 7
10. 6
11. 6
12. 5
13. 2
14. 4
15. 4
16. 3
17. 5
18. 2
19. 6
20. 4
21. 16
22. 9
23. 11
24. 11

Page 30
1. 3
2. 40
3. 9
4. 2
5. 5
6. 16
7. 4
8. 8
9. 2
10. 2
11. 60
12. 30
13. 3
14. 24
15. 6
16. 3
17. 6
18. 9
19. 4
20. 7
21. 4
22. 5
23. 11
24. 7

Page 31
1. (14, 16, 18, 20, 22)
2. (13, 15, 17, 19, 21)
3. (21, 25, 29, 33, 37)
4. (24, 28, 32, 36, 40)
5. (30, 35, 40, 45, 50)
6. (31, 36, 41, 46, 51)
7. (6, 4, 2, 0)
8. (50, 40, 30, 20, 10)
9. (500, 600, 700, 800, 900)
10. (56, 76, 86, 96, 106)
11. (44, 66, 77, 88, 99, 110)
12. (22, 29, 37, 46, 56)
13. (32, 64, 128, 256)
14. (125, 150, 175, 200, 225)
15. (36, 45, 55, 66, 78)

Page 32
1. triangle, circle, square
2. hexagon, triangle, triangle
3. C, A, C, A, B, C
4. AA, BB, BB, AA, BB
5. 58, 68, 78, 88, 98
6. RR, SS, TT, UU, VV
7. square, square
8. TTT, SS, TTT, R, SS
9. PP, G, PP, PP, G
10. 50, 25, 50, 75
11. RR, SSS, SS, TTT, TT, UUU
12. 30, 20, 30, 10, 20
13. 10, 5, 10, 20
14. square, circle
15. upside-down triangle, triangle, triangle

Page 33
1. 9
2. 3
3. 22
4. 3
5. 7
6. 1
7. 70
8. 53
9. 75
10. 15
11. 7
12. 41
13. 40
14. 7
15. 53
16. 20
17. 8
18. 11
19. 17
20. 21
21. 46

Page 34
1. 4
2. 7
3. 24
4. 16
5. 64
6. 9
7. 1
8. 69
9. 40
10. 29
11. 8
12. 40
13. 0
14. 14
15. 6
16. 25
17. 7
18. 30
19. 79
20. 24
21. 30

Page 35
1. 9, 10, 11
2. 13, 15, 18
3. 5, 6, 7, 8
4. 17, 19, 21, 24
5. 14, 16, 18, 22
6. 5, 7, 8, 9
7. 15, 21, 24, 27
8. 10, 12, 16, 18

Page 36
1. 7, 8, 9, 10
2. 3, 4, 5, 6
3. 5, 6, 7, 8
4. 3, 4, 5, 6
5. 15, 21, 24, 27, 36
6. 6, 8, 10, 11, 14
7. 15, 16, 17
8. 5, 7, 8

Page 37
1. 14, 16, 22, 24
2. 25, 30, 35, 40
3. 30, 40, 60, 70
4. 8, 9, 10, 11
5. 16, 28, 32, 36
6. 15, 18, 19, 22
7. 13, 16, 19, 20
8. 26, 29, 32, 35

Page 38
1. $n = 18$
2. $n = 14$
3. $n = 15$
4. $c = 19$
5. $b = 13$
6. $n = 19$
7. $a = 18$
8. $d = 20$
9. $n = 20$
10. $t = 14$
11. $s = 12$
12. $d = 15$
13. $r = 15$
14. $c = 15$
15. $n = 21$
16. $s = 16$
17. $n = 30$
18. $d = 29$

Page 39
1. $n = 20$
2. $n = 38$
3. $t = 20$
4. $d = 26$
5. $n = 20$
6. $c = 21$
7. $t = 32$
8. $b = 21$
9. $s = 40$
10. $n = 27$
11. $x = 14$
12. $r = 27$
13. $n = 45$
14. $d = 32$
15. $t = 24$
16. $n = 25$
17. $p = 30$
18. $b = 30$

Page 40
1. A
2. C
3. C
4. C

5. A
6. B
7. A
8. A
9. B
10. D
11. B
12. B
13. D
14. B
15. D
16. C

Page 41
1. C
2. B
3. A
4. C
5. B
6. B
7. C
8. A
9. A
10. A
11. D
12. B
13. D
14. B
15. C
16. A

Page 42
1. B
2. D
3. D
4. C
5. A
6. C
7. B
8. A
9. B
10. D
11. D
12. D
13. C
14. B

Page 43
1. C
2. B
3. D
4. A
5. A
6. C
7. B
8. A
9. A
10. B
11. B
12. C
13. B
14. C

Page 44
1. C
2. D
3. B
4. A
5. C
6. B
7. D
8. C
9. B
10. A

Page 45
1. B
2. A
3. D
4. D
5. D
6. D
7. B
8. A
9. C
10. B
11. D
12. C